We Can Do It
and
The Big Jump

'We Can Do It' and 'The Big Jump'
An original concept by Jenny Jinks
© Jenny Jinks

Illustrated by Laura Estrada Ferraz

Published by MAVERICK ARTS PUBLISHING LTD
Studio 11, City Business Centre, 6 Brighton Road,
Horsham, West Sussex, RH13 5BB
© Maverick Arts Publishing Limited November 2019
+44 (0)1403 256941

A CIP catalogue record for this book is available at the British Library.

ISBN 978-1-84886-625-6

www.maverickbooks.co.uk

This book is rated as: Red Band (Guided Reading)
This story is decodable at Letters and Sounds Phase 2.

We Can Do It
and
The Big Jump

By Jenny Jinks

Illustrated by
Laura Estrada
Ferraz

The Letter A

Trace the lower and upper case letter with a finger. Sound out the letter.

Around,
up,
down

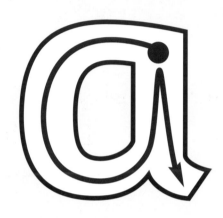

Down,
up,
down,
lift,
cross

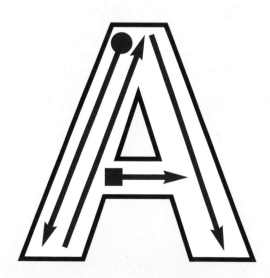

Some words to familiarise:

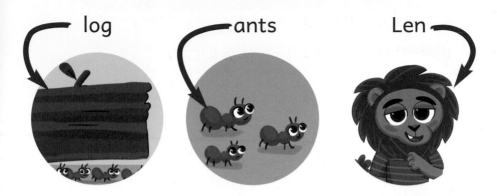

log   ants   Len

High-frequency words:

a   into   the   I   said   was

it   we   no   you   they   up

Tips for Reading 'We Can Do It'

- Practise the words listed above before reading the story.

- If the reader struggles with any of the other words, ask them to look for sounds they know in the word. Encourage them to sound out the words and help them read the words if necessary.

- After reading the story, ask the reader why the ants are able to lift the log.

Fun Activity

Look under a rock and see what insects there are!

We Can Do It

A log fell into the pond.

"I am King," said Len.
"I will do it."

"I am strong," said Hal.
"I will do it."

But the log was stuck.

"I am big," said Ella.
"I will do it."

But the log was stuck.

13

"We can do it," said the ants.

"No, not you," said the animals.

The ants got the log.

They lifted it up.

"You did it!"

The Letter J

Trace the lower and upper case letter with a finger. Sound out the letter.

*Down,
around,
lift,
dot*

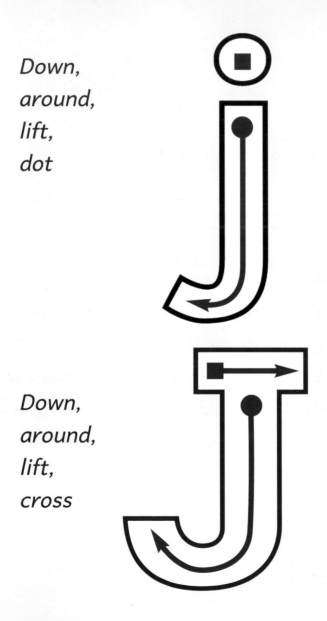

*Down,
around,
lift,
cross*

Some words to familiarise:

Mel   Jack   Fizz

High-frequency words:

I a up the said she was

Tips for Reading 'The Big Jump'

- Practise the words listed above before reading the story.

- If the reader struggles with any of the other words, ask them to look for sounds they know in the word. Encourage them to sound out the words and help them read the words if necessary.

- After reading the story, ask the reader who jumped the highest.

Fun Activity

Jump as high as you can!

The Big Jump

"I can do a jump," said Mel.

Mel went up the ramp.
Zip, zap!

21

Mel did a hop.

Jack went up the ramp. Dash!

Fizz went up the ramp. Rush!

She went up... up... up!

"I cannot get down!"

Book Bands for Guided Reading

The Institute of Education book banding system is a scale of colours that reflects the various levels of reading difficulty. The bands are assigned by taking into account the content, the language style, the layout and phonics. Word, phrase and sentence level work is also taken into consideration.

Maverick Early Readers are a bright, attractive range of books covering the pink to white bands. All of these books have been book banded for guided reading to the industry standard and edited by a leading educational consultant.

To view the whole Maverick Readers scheme, visit our website at
www.maverickearlyreaders.com

Or scan the QR code above to view our scheme instantly!

Pink
Red
Yellow
Blue
Green
Orange
Turquoise
Purple
Gold
White